p

Parragon
Queen Street House
4 Queen Street
Bath BA1 1HE, UK

This is a Parragon book
First published in 2006
ISBN: 1-40548-511-6
Printed in Italy

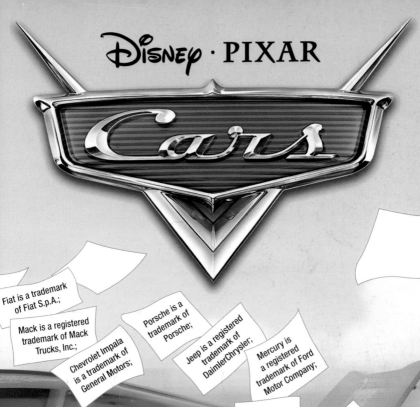

Disney · PIXAR

Cars

-Contents-

Lightning McQueen

McQueen is a hotshot rookie race car on the Piston Cup series. He has made a name for himself with his amazing driving and is tied with The King and Chick Hicks for first place going into the last race of the year. His eye is on the prize, and nothing else matters.

Chick Hicks

A veteran on the Piston Cup circuit, he has always finished second to The King and has a big chip on his shoulder because of it. All Chick wants in life is to win the Piston Cup and get the coveted Dinoco sponsorship - and he will stop at nothing to get them. He hates McQueen for stealing his thunder.

Strip "The King" Weathers

This 1970 Plymouth Superbird is a legend in his own time. The King has won more Piston Cups than any other racer, but he's also always kept his priorities straight. He knows a champion comes from practise, teamwork and a true heart.

Sally

A Porsche 911, Sally lost her appetite for life in the California fast lane and found the speed of Radiator Springs much more to her liking. Her goal is to put Radiator Springs back on the map.

Mater

Mater is the sweetest and most loyal guy in Radiator Springs and the first to see McQueen for who he really is. A good-ol'-boy tow truck with a big heart, Mater loves tractor-tipping.

Doc Hudson

A 1951 Hudson Hornet, Doc Hudson is the town doctor and the town judge. He looks out for the townsfolk and their best interests. He is the heart of Radiator Springs with a mysterious past he is trying to escape.

Sheriff

The law in Radiator Springs is a 1949 Mercury police cruiser. Though Sheriff may eat a few too many doughnuts, he still takes his job seriously and is ready to catch anyone speeding through town.

Sarge

This surly 1942 WWII Willys Army Jeep is the owner of the local army surplus store and an extremely patriotic veteran. He can often be found arguing with his neighbour Fillmore.

Fillmore

Fillmore is a 1960 VW Bus that is stuck in the '60s. He brews his own organic fuel, which he sells from the tie-dyed dome he lives in. He drives Sarge nuts with his conspiracy theories and his hippie ways.

Luigi

Luigi is a 1959 Fiat 500 who owns the local tyre shop, Luigi's Casa Della Tyres, "Home of the Leaning Tower of Tyres." He is an avid fan of Ferraris.

Guido

This little Italian forklift is Luigi's best friend and helps out at the tyre shop. The only word Guido knows in English is "pit stop."

Flo

Flo is a 1950s show car who was passing through
Radiator Springs on tour when she saw Ramone. It
was love at first sight and she has never left. She
runs the local diner, Flo's V8 Café, serving
the finest fuel in fifty states.

Ramone

This 1959 Impala is the town's resident artist. He owns
and operates Ramone's House of Body Art, the local
custom body and paint shop. He only has eyes for Flo.

Red

Though Red might not say much, he is always ready to help his neighbours if anyone needs it. He spends his days nurturing the flowers he plants around town.

Lizzie

Lizzie is the oldest resident of Radiator Springs and often talks of her romantic dates with the town founder, Stanley. Forgetful and brash, Lizzie runs the curio shop.

At the Dinoco 400...

WELCOME BACK...

HE'S LOST ANOTHER TYRE! THE KING AND CHICK ARE COMING UP FAST!

SCEEEEEE!

GASP!

IT'S TOO CLOSE TO CALL!

24

THE ROAD
TO
CALIFORNIA

JUST STOPPING OFF FOR A QUICK BREATHER, KID.

...until nightfall, when Mack finally needs a rest.

ABSOLUTELY NOT! WE'RE DRIVING ALL NIGHT!

DOIIIING!

When it is all over, McQueen is left dangling from telephone wires and the road is ruined.

BOY, YOU'RE IN A HEAP OF TROUBLE!

33

BREAKING
Racing Television
RTV
LIVE
RACE CAR LIGHTNING MCQUEEN IS REPORTED MISSING...
MCQUEEN IS SCHEDULED TO RACE IN AN UNPRECEDENTED TIE-BREAKING EVENT...
MCQUEEN'S SPONSORS STATED THEY HAVE NO IDEA WHERE HE IS!

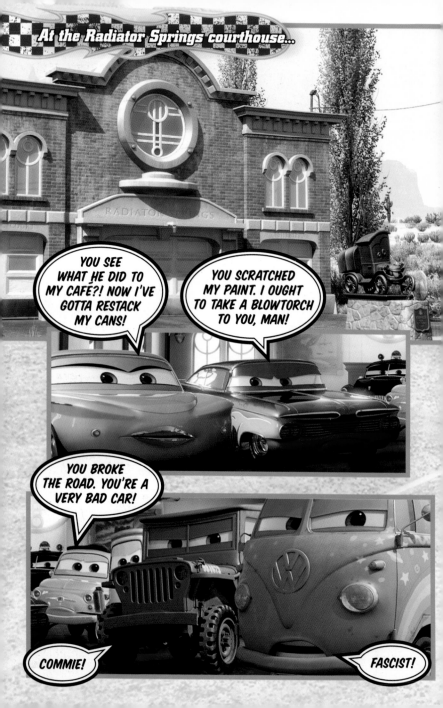

Suddenly, the courtroom doors swing open and in comes a beautiful Porsche 911.
JUSTITAE VIA STRATA VERITATE
SORRY I'M LATE, YOUR HONOUR.
HE'S LETTING ME GO.
ACCUSED
HE'S LETTING YOU GO?
WHAT DO YOU WANT, SALLY?

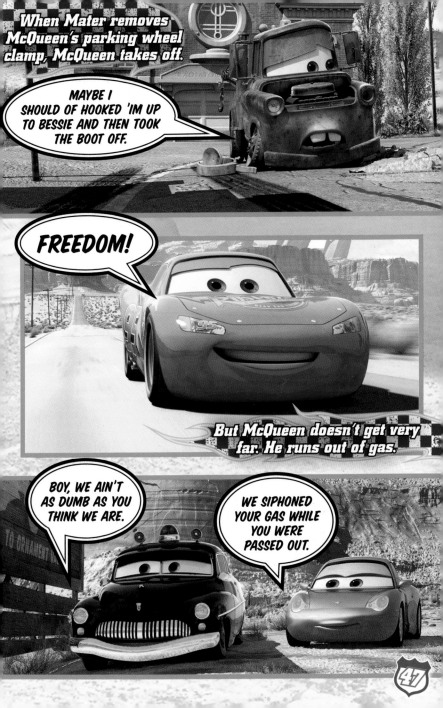

When Mater removes McQueen's parking wheel clamp, McQueen takes off.

MAYBE I SHOULD OF HOOKED 'IM UP TO BESSIE AND THEN TOOK THE BOOT OFF.

FREEDOM!

But McQueen doesn't get very far. He runs out of gas.

BOY, WE AIN'T AS DUMB AS YOU THINK WE ARE.

WE SIPHONED YOUR GAS WHILE YOU WERE PASSED OUT.

47

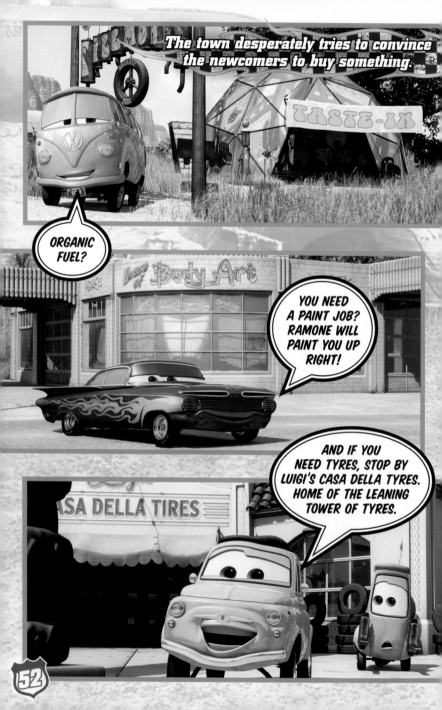

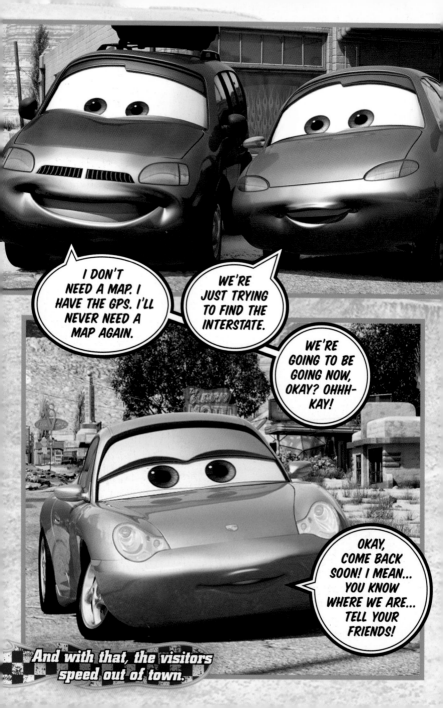

I DON'T NEED A MAP. I HAVE THE GPS. I'LL NEVER NEED A MAP AGAIN.

WE'RE JUST TRYING TO FIND THE INTERSTATE.

WE'RE GOING TO BE GOING NOW, OKAY? OHHH-KAY!

OKAY, COME BACK SOON! I MEAN... YOU KNOW WHERE WE ARE... TELL YOUR FRIENDS!

And with that, the visitors speed out of town.

Meanwhile, McQueen speeds around Willys Butte.

As he rounds the final curve...

...he loses control, slides off the road into a gorge and lands in a cactus patch.

ZOOOM!

SHERIFF, IS HE MAKING ANOTHER RUN FOR IT?

NO, NO. HE RAN OUT OF ASPHALT IN THE MIDDLE OF THE NIGHT AND ASKED ME IF HE COULD COME DOWN HERE. ALL HE'S TRYING TO DO IS MAKE THAT THERE TURN.

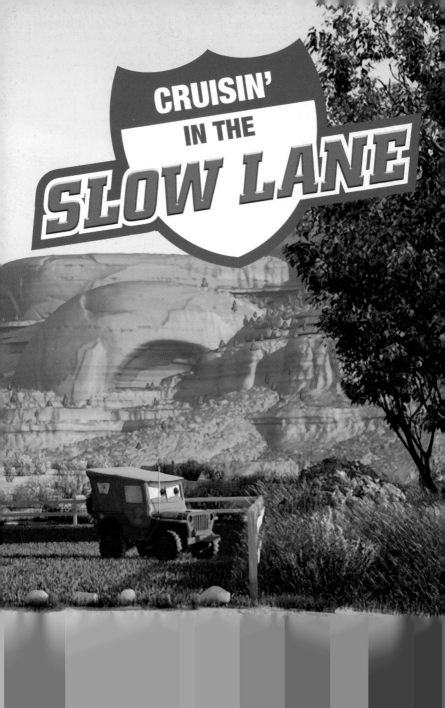

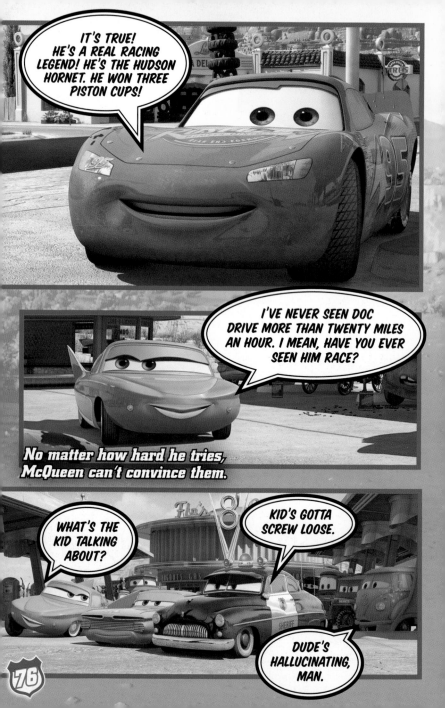

IT'S TRUE! HE'S A REAL RACING LEGEND! HE'S THE HUDSON HORNET. HE WON THREE PISTON CUPS!

I'VE NEVER SEEN DOC DRIVE MORE THAN TWENTY MILES AN HOUR. I MEAN, HAVE YOU EVER SEEN HIM RACE?

No matter how hard he tries, McQueen can't convince them.

WHAT'S THE KID TALKING ABOUT?

KID'S GOTTA SCREW LOOSE.

DUDE'S HALLUCINATING, MAN.

Later that afternoon, McQueen finds
Doc secretly racing on the track.

VROOM!

WOOOSH!

ZOOOOM!

77

SCREEEECH!

WOW! YOU'RE AMAZING!

When Doc realizes McQueen is watching, he turns around and leaves.

95

McQueen starts thinking about his friends in Radiator Springs. Winning just isn't that important to him anymore.

NATIONAL S

Suddenly, McQueen almost slams into a wall! Then McQueen hears a voice on his radio.

I DIDN'T COME ALL THIS WAY TO SEE YOU QUIT. ALRIGHT, IF YOU CAN DRIVE AS GOOD AS YOU CAN FIX A ROAD, THEN YOU CAN WIN THIS RACE WITH YOUR EYES SHUT. NOW GET BACK OUT THERE!

FABULOUS HUDSON HORNET

Rust-eze

95   Lightning McQueen   95

Doc and the townsfolk have come to be McQueen's pit crew! With a renewed spirit, McQueen tears back onto the track.

85

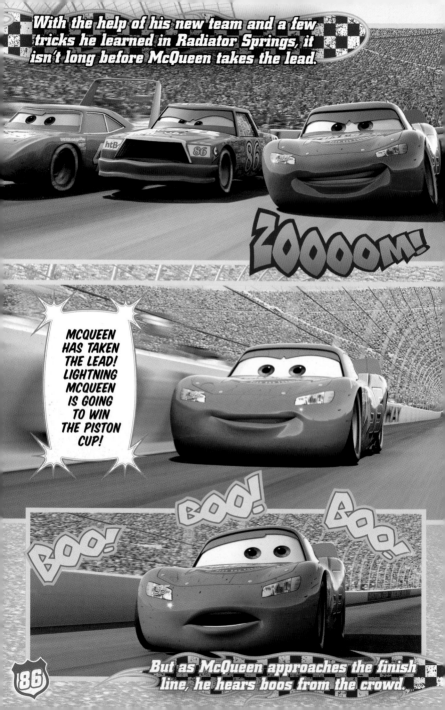

With the help of his new team and a few tricks he learned in Radiator Springs, it isn't long before McQueen takes the lead.

ZOOOOM!

MCQUEEN HAS TAKEN THE LEAD! LIGHTNING MCQUEEN IS GOING TO WIN THE PISTON CUP!

BOO! BOO! BOO!

But as McQueen approaches the finish line, he hears boos from the crowd.

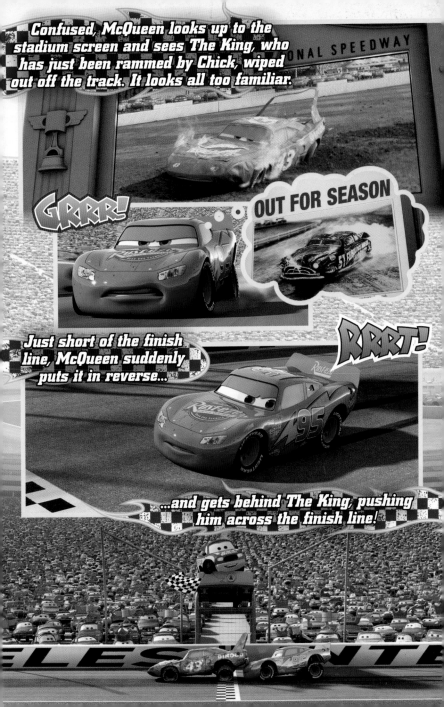

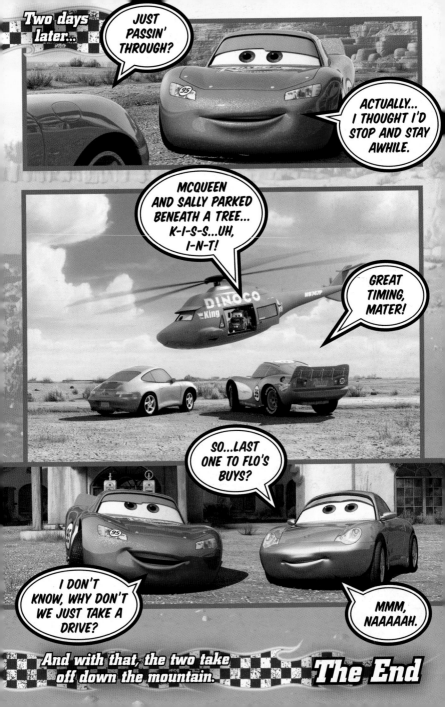

Ramone is a 1959 two-door hardtop Impala. This '59 model is often referred to as bat-winged because of the rear styling. Some Impalas have hydraulics installed that allow the car to drive on three wheels, allowing the front end to bounce up and down or the entire car to lift.

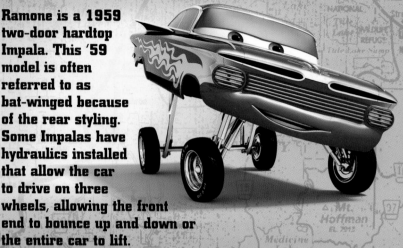

Doc Hudson is a 1951 Hudson Hornet. This popular stock car did actually race on the NASCAR circuit the year the Hornet came out and won the Grand National race many times over.

This model featured an extra-high rear wing and a pointed nose. The Superbird with the 426 Hemi engine is considered by some to be the most valuable muscle car ever made. It was designed for NASCAR, but was also available to the public. This car was only made in 1970.

Sarge is a 1942 World War II Willys Army Jeep, also known as the Willys Jeep, GI Jeep, World War II Jeep, or just plain Army Jeep. This model saw lots of action in World War II.

Fillmore is a 1960 Volkswagen Bus. Volkswagen means "the people's car" in German, which makes sense, since Volkswagen made inexpensive cars that anyone could afford. During the late '60s and early '70s, the Bus was considered the car of the hippie.

Luigi is a 1959 Fiat 500, a tiny economy car that could fit four people, just not their luggage. Due to the Fiat 500's size, some models came with roof racks for added storage – though others came with a large sunroof like Luigi's instead.

CARS BOOK OF THE FILM

READ ALL ABOUT LIGHTNING MCQUEEN'S LIFE-CHANGING ADVENTURE IN THIS NOT-TO-BE-MISSED ACTION-PACKED NOVEL!

CARS MAGICAL STORYBOOK

CHILDREN OF ALL AGES WILL LOVE READING OR LISTENING TO THIS FAST-PACED DISNEY ADVENTURE.

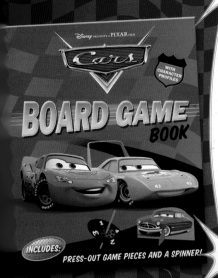

CARS BOARD GAME BOOK

RACE CARS WERE BORN TO RACE! PICK YOUR FAVOURITE CAR AND GUIDE IT AROUND THE TRACK. YOU'LL NEED STEELY NERVES, QUICK THINKING AND A BIT OF LUCK TO WIN THIS RACE. SO START YOUR ENGINES AND GET GOING IN THIS FANTASTIC FOLD-OUT STRATEGY GAME.

CARS STICKER SCENE

READ THIS FUN STORY TO FIND OUT WHAT HAPPENS TO LIGHTNING McQUEEN ON HIS WAY TO THE BIG RACE, THEN USE THE FOLD-OUT STICKER SCENES TO CREATE YOUR OWN CARS ADVENTURES!

CARS STICKER ACTIVITY BOOK

HAVE HOURS OF FUN COMPLETING THESE ACTIVITIES, INCLUDING MAZES, WORD SEARCHES, CODE-BREAKERS AND MUCH, MUCH MORE!

INCLUDES: MAZES, PUZZLES, STICKERS AND MORE!

DISNEY PRESENTS A PIXAR FILM